The fur - ther you take my rights a - way   the fast - er I will run.

The fur - ther you take my rights a - way   the fast - er I will run.

The fur - ther you take my rights a - way____   the fast - er I will run.

You can de - ny me,   you can de - cide   to

You can de - ny   me,   you can de - cide   to

You can de - ny   me,   you can de - cide   to

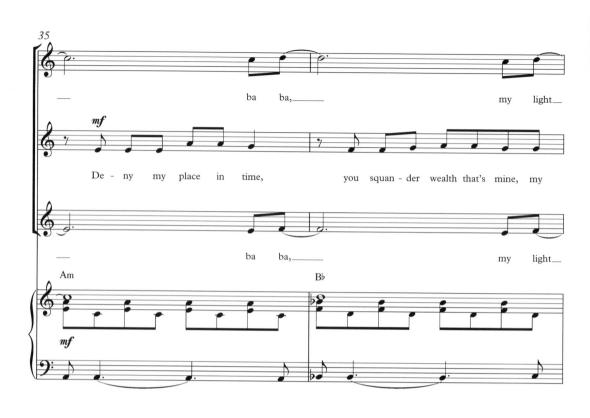

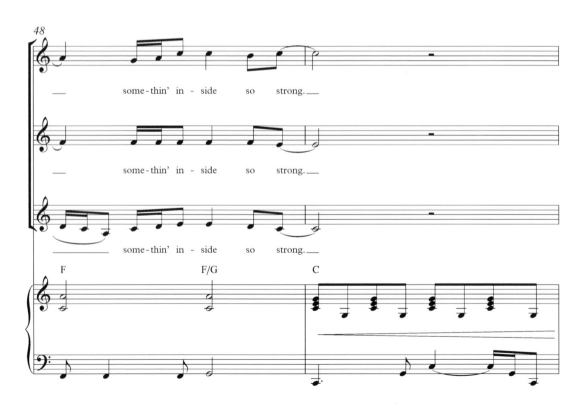

50

f

Ah.

f

Bro-thers and sis-ters when they in-sist we're just not good e-nough,

f

Ah.

Bb   F/A   C   F/C

f

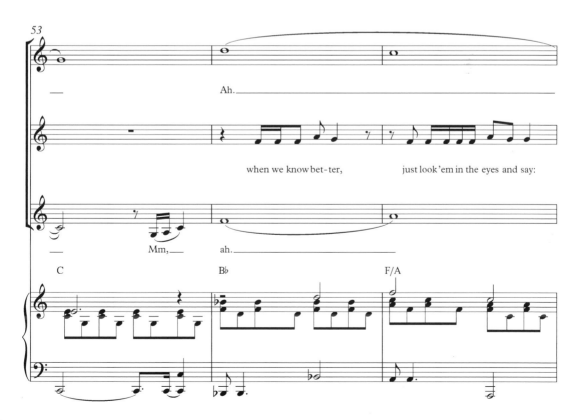

53

Ah.

when we know bet-ter, just look 'em in the eyes and say:

Mm, ah.

C   Bb   F/A

(SOMETHING INSIDE) SO STRONG IS A POWERFUL SONG OF HOPE AND STRENGTH IN ADVERSITY AND IS BRITISH SINGER-SONGWRITER LABI SIFFRE'S BIGGEST HIT TO DATE. WRITTEN AS AN ANTI-APARTHEID ANTHEM FOR SOUTH AFRICA IN 1987, THE LYRICS ARE APPLICABLE TO ALL WHO WISH TO RISE UP FROM THEIR OPPRESSION.

THE STRONG MESSAGE IS ENCAPSULATED HERE IN RICH HARMONIES FOR SSA CHOIR WITH PIANO ACCOMPANIMENT.

ALSO AVAILABLE FROM MUSIC SALES:

BEAUTIFUL (CHRISTINA AGUILERA)
SATB/PIANO – NOV170533
SSA/PIANO – NOV170544

BLACKBIRD (THE BEATLES)
SATB/PIANO – NO91300
SSA/PIANO – NO91289

DON'T STOP BELIEVIN' (JOURNEY)
SSA/PIANO – NOV941402
SAB/PIANO – NOV941435

FIELDS OF GOLD (STING)
SATB/PIANO – NOV940907
SSA/PIANO – NOV940918

HALLELUJAH (LEONARD COHEN, JEFF BUCKLEY AND OTHERS)
SATB/PIANO – NOV940863
SSA/PIANO – NOV940874

HERO (MARIAH CAREY, X FACTOR FINALISTS)
SATB/PIANO – NOV940830
SSA/PIANO – NOV940841

I HAVE A DREAM (ABBA)
SATB/PIANO – NOV170467
SSA/PIANO – NOV170478

MAN IN THE MIRROR (MICHAEL JACKSON)
SATB/PIANO – NOV941281
SSA/PIANO – NOV941094

REJOICE (KATHERINE JENKINS, IL DIVO)
SATB/PIANO – NOV940819

RULE THE WORLD (TAKE THAT)
SATB/PIANO – NOV940940
SSA/PIANO – NOV940951

RUN (SNOW PATROL, LEONA LEWIS)
SATB/PIANO – NOV940852

WONDERFUL TONIGHT (ERIC CLAPTON)
SATB/PIANO – NOV170489
SSA/PIANO – NOV170511

YOU RAISE ME UP (JOSH GROBAN, WESTLIFE AND OTHERS)
SATB/PIANO – NOV940929
SSA/PIANO – NOV940896

Novello Publishing Limited
part of The Music Sales Group
14-15 Berners Street
London W1T 3LJ, UK

Exclusive distributors:
Music Sales Limited
Newmarket Road
Bury St Edmunds
Suffolk IP33 3YB, UK
www.chesternovello.com
This publication © 2011
Novello & Company Limited

ISBN 978-1-84938-187-1

9 781849 381871